£7.95
HW/TE

NOVELLO HANDEL EDITION
General Editor Watkins Shaw

Messiah

a sacred oratorio for soprano, alto, tenor & bass soli,
SATB & orchestra

Words selected from Holy Scripture by Charles Jennens

Edited by Watkins Shaw

vocal score

NOVELLO

London and Sevenoaks

783-3

MAJORA CANAMUS

(Virgil, *Eclogue IV*)

And without Controversy, great is the mystery of Godliness:

God was manifested in the Flesh, justified by the Spirit, seen of Angels, preached among the Gentiles, believed on in the world, received up in glory.

In whom are hid all the Treasures of Wisdom and Knowledge.

(1 Timothy iii, 16; Colossians ii, 3)

These words, selected by Jennens, the librettist, formed a preface to the word-book of the first performance in April 1742, at Dublin. They were repeated on the word-books published in London 1749-59 and later.

Paperback Edition Cat. No. 07 0137

Case bound Edition Cat. No. 07 0137 01

It is requested that on all concert notices and programmes reference should be made to 'Shaw's edition (Novello & Co., Ltd.)'.

PREFACE

For every movement included in this edition (save one), there exists Handel's original autograph, and on that authoritative basis this edition rests. (The exception is the C minor version of ' How beautiful are the feet '.) Full details of the sources, the derivation of the transposed versions, and the reasons for the selection now presented from among several versions of certain numbers, together with many other matters, are set out in *A Textual Companion to Handel's ' Messiah '*, which is being issued in connexion with this edition.*

Here it must suffice to state shortly that, apart from the piano/organ part in the vocal score (which is, of course, an arrangement), everything possible has been done to reflect the autographs precisely. At the same time, this is a practical edition, and the notation used by Handel has therefore been interpreted for use in performances today. But in every instance the user of this edition will be able at a glance to distinguish between Handel's autograph text and the editor's suggestions, and thus know exactly where he stands.

The following items explain the editor's procedure:

1. Time-signatures. 4/4 in this edition represents Handel's C. But C has been retained as the conventional signature for *recitativo secco*. Any other departure from Handel's signatures is noted in its place in the text.

2. Accidentals. Accidentals not found in the autographs are placed by the editor in brackets. Redundant accidentals are, of course, eliminated.

3. Barring, and ' underlaying ' of words. These are discussed in the *Textual Companion*.

4. *Appoggiature* and ' graces '. The occasional *appoggiature* found in the autographs are each marked where they occur in the text. All other *appoggiature*, and all ' graces ', are editorial, whether they are shown on the main stave or in the form of an *ossia*.

5. Shakes. Handel's shake-marks are carefully reproduced; those added by the editor are placed in square brackets.

6. Marks of speed, style and dynamics. Handel's own directions of speed and style are printed in bold type. His dynamic marks, however he expressed them, are expanded to the full form of the word, as *piano*, *fortissimo*, etc. Thus, any marks in the abbreviated form, *p*, *ff*, etc., are editorial.

*Subsequently published as *A Textual and Historical Companion to Handel's 'Messiah'* by Watkins Shaw (Novello & Co., 1965).

7. Clef-signs. Where, in solo numbers, Handel used clef-signs other than the G or F clefs, these are shewn on a preliminary stave. The alto and tenor parts of the choruses are written in the appropriate C clefs in the autographs, but are rendered here by the clefs 𝄞 and 𝄞 respectively.

8. Rhythmic interpretation. The editor has made his suggestions for the interpretation of the loose rhythmic notation of the eighteenth century in these ways:

(a) Wherever the following notation is found (♩ . . ♬ or ⌐· ♪), it is to be understood that the autographs read (♩ . ♪ or ⌐ ♪). Neither double dots nor dotted rests were used by Handel. On the other hand, the notation (⌐ ⌐ ♪) is from the autograph.

(b) Other alterations are suggested by rhythmic signs placed above or below Handel's notation. These rhythmic signs consist of the usual notation without the note-head itself, thus:

$$\text{|} \quad \text{|.} \quad \ulcorner \quad \ulcorner \quad \ulcorner\urcorner \quad \ulcorner . \urcorner$$

These should be self-explanatory.

In every instance, therefore, Handel's notation either is preserved exactly, or can be readily reconstructed.

THE PIANO/ORGAN ARRANGEMENT

Every such arrangement in the vocal scores known to the editor is designed for the pianoforte, for rehearsal purposes only. But the fact remains, whether or not one considers it desirable, that innumerable performances of *Messiah*, in whole or in part, are given year by year to an organ, not an orchestral, accompaniment.

With this in mind, the editor has here attempted the (admittedly thankless) task of devising an arrangement which, while still being useful for pianoforte rehearsal, yet gives more assistance to the organist than hitherto. Its dual role should be thus interpreted: *Pianists*—Where all the notes on the lower stave cannot be played by the left hand, and the right hand is not free to render assistance, the accompaniment will sound reasonably complete for rehearsal purposes if the left hand neglects the notes with upward stems and plays the bass line only. The only exception will be No. 20, in which it will often be convenient to take the bass an octave higher in order to play all four parts. *Organists*—The bass line should be played on the pedals, the notes on the lower stave with upward stems being intended for the left hand.

A piano/organ arrangement must do duty both for Handel's instrumental score and for the *continuo* filling-in as well. In this edition, small-size notes are used to represent the latter, and organists will be able to play them on another manual, so as to throw the *obbligato* parts (including the bass) into relief. It must be emphasised that this in no way provides a true *continuo* part to be used with orchestra; only what can be contrived on two staves between the pitch of the *obbligato* parts. Two small points should be explained: first, that the oboe parts (which Handel did not generally write, but left to be supplied by others) are not treated as *obbligato*, so that when oboes play alone in unison with the voices, they are not reproduced as part of the piano/organ arrangement; second, that where the complete orchestra is engaged, the very occasional 'filling-in' notes are not distinguished by the use of small-size notes.

The whole of the piano/organ part is, of course, frankly an arrangement, and not a compression of Handel's score. The bass part, however, is literally transcribed as to pitch, though not as to repetition of notes. When playing it on the pedals, organists may well find it convenient to take some notes in a different octave. The figuring of the bass is that of the autographs; for this reason, no figures will be found in the transposed versions. Handel's slurs (bowing marks) are carefully reproduced. Those supplied editorially (usually of a *simile* character) are shown with a short stroke, thus ⁀‖⁀ in the ingenious manner devised by Mr. Thurston Dart.

The expressions *con Ripieno* and *senza Ripieno* and the like are derived from Handel's own markings in his 'conducting score'. (See the *Textual Companion*.) These are reproduced (for the first time in the accompaniment to a vocal score) to enable organists to introduce appropriate contrasts in tone. When placed in square brackets they are the responsibility of the editor.*

ACKNOWLEDGMENTS

I acknowledge with humble gratitude my indebtedness to Her Majesty Queen Elizabeth II for gracious permission to use Handel's original autograph score at a time preceding her gift of this, together with the rest of the Royal Music Library, to the British Museum in 1958.

To my colleagues the Warden and Fellows of St. Michael's College, Tenbury Wells, Worcestershire, I am indebted for permission to use Handel's 'conducting score' of *Messiah*.

WATKINS SHAW

Worcester
23 June 1958

*But see remarks (1981) on p.viii.

NOTE TO THE 1981 REVISION

In a period of 22 years since this edition appeared and more than 25 years since it was begun, the editor may be permitted some second thoughts. In that same period, too, the climate in which *Messiah* is performed has changed — perhaps, as I should like to think, in modest measure on account of this very edition. The present issue provides an opportunity to correct a few slips, make a few adjustments, and also to offer some observations.

RHYTHMIC ALTERATION (see paragraph 8, p. iv above). I have modified some rather impractical interpretations in 'Behold the Lamb of God' (bars 19, 20, 24, 25). This movement (in which I am certainly not the first to advocate over-dotting) continues to excite controversy, based in part on the clash at the end of bars 2 and 5, but I adhere to my view of it in relation to Largo style, while pleading for the avoidance of a military march interpretation and suggesting a relaxation drawing near to compound time. For the rest, here and elsewhere, I do not repent of my marks which experience tells might have been extended, and I trust conductors will in fact do this.

ORNAMENTS. Ornamentation is a matter for spontaneity in performance, not editorial fiat. My intention in 1959 was to do no more than point the way, and it is gratifying to notice the increasing number of singers now able to 'grace' their lines stylishly and introduce cadenzas different from and more numerous than those tentatively introduced here. *Performance of embellishments not found here does not invalidate this edition as such*, for it is proper to the individual singer, not the printed page.

RECITATIVE CADENCES. In 1959, according to long-standing practice, I indicated postponement of final cadences in all recitatives. Almost immediately I bitterly regretted this in No. 14(b) and am glad now to have the chance to adjust it. There has since been a good deal of attention to evidence that such cadences were by no means invariably postponed. Telemann draws a distinction between opera (non-postponed) and cantata (postponed), leaving the awkward question of how Handel, a primarily dramatic composer, regarded his oratorios. There is an excellent discussion of the matter in Robert Donington, *The Interpretation of Music* (New Version, 1974), and one readily endorses his sensible conclusion that the deciding factor is one of pace in transition from one movement to another. Even so, that leaves many instances to be settled by personal taste. In accordance with my present view, I have adjusted not only No. 14(b) but also Nos 15, 29, 42, 47, and 49. I leave untouched the postponed form in Nos 2, 5, 8, and 31, which some conductors may prefer to adjust.

ALTERNATIVE VERSIONS. This edition classifies these into (a) those of equal authority in Handel's own usage, printed here in the main body of the text; (b) those of doubtful, but not impossible standing, printed here in the Appendix; (c) those which there is strong evidence that Handel came to reject, and so are not included here (though given in my *Textual and Historical Companion*). Of late years, perhaps in pursuit of novelty, there has been a tendency for performances to draw on (c), even using versions of 'But who may abide' and 'How beautiful are the feet' which there is the strongest presumption that Handel never performed, and of 'And lo, the angel of the Lord' which he only temporarily used and then abandoned. In my opinion this is to be deprecated; for though there is indeed no single form of the work as a whole which is final (and this edition provides material for considerable variety), yet it misrepresents a master composer to put out his work including material he himself rejected.

'SENZA RIPIENO' DIRECTIONS. For a note on these, see p. viii.

Worcester   WATKINS SHAW
12 March 1981

ALLOCATION OF SOLO WORK

Conductors are invited to note and carefully consider the following matters:

1. The version here given of ' But who may abide ' in D minor was written for an alto. Its first singer was a male alto, Guadagni; but Handel also had it sung by a woman alto. He also authorised its transposition for soprano. There is not one shred of evidence that he ever gave it to a bass.

2. Handel from time to time allotted tenor numbers to a soprano. In particular, concerning ' Thy rebuke ', ' Behold and see ', ' He was cut off ' and ' But thou didst not leave ', he frequently had them sung in one of the two following ways:

	A	or	B
Thy rebuke	Tenor		Soprano 1
Behold and see	Tenor		Soprano 1
He was cut off	Soprano		Soprano 2
But thou didst not leave	Soprano		Soprano 2

3. The employment of two soprano soloists (one of whom was sometimes a boy) was a common practice of Handel's in this work.

4. Four possible schemes of alternative allocations of certain numbers are appended. Whilst there is admittedly an element of conjecture (though based on a careful examination of available evidence) in the first three of these, it is quite certain that Handel himself constantly re-allocated the solo work on some such lines as these. Hence we depart entirely from the spirit of his performances if, year after year, we follow a rigidly unchanging assignment of numbers to the customary solo quartet. But it has to be observed that there is no evidence to show that Handel changed the work of the bass soloist from 1750 onwards.

Scheme I is based on the editor's conjectured reconstruction of the cast for the year 1750. (See ' A Handelian Team of *Messiah* Singers: 1749 or 1750?' in *The Monthly Musical Record*, vol. 88, p. 169, 1958.) Schemes II and III are based on the editor's conjectured reconstruction of the cast for the years 1752 and 1753. (See ' Covent Garden Performances of *Messiah* in 1749, 1752 and 1753 ' in *The Music Review*, vol. XIX, p. 85, May 1958.) Scheme IV is based on the set of parts belonging to the Thomas Coram Foundation (the Foundling Hospital), and relates probably to the year 1754, certainly not earlier.

	I	II	III	IV
Comfort ye /Every valley	T.	T.	T.	T.
Thus saith the Lord	B.	B.	B.	B.
But who may abide	CT.	A.	CT.	S.2
Behold, a virgin /O thou that tellest	A.	A.	CT.	A.
For behold, darkness /The people that walked	B.	B.	B.	B.
There were shepherds /And lo, the angel / And the angel /And suddenly	Boy	S.	S.	S.1
Rejoice greatly	S.	S.	S.	S.1
Then shall the eyes /He shall feed	CT.	S.	CT.	S.1
Come unto him	S.(?)	S.	CT.(?)	S.1

	I	II	III	IV
He was despised	CT.	A.	CT.	A.
All they that see him	T.	T.	T.	T.
Thy rebuke/Behold and see	S.	T.	T.	T.
He was cut off/But thou didst not leave	Boy	S.	S.	S.1
Unto which of the angels	T.	T.	T.	T.
Thou art gone up	CT.	A.	CT.	S.2
How beautiful	S.	S.	CT.	S.1
Why do the nations	B.	B.	B.	B.
He that dwelleth/Thou shalt break them	T.	T.	T.	T.
I know that my redeemer liveth	S.	S.	S.	S.1
Behold, I tell you/The trumpet shall sound	B.	B.	B.	B.
Then shall be brought	A.	A.	CT.	A.
O death, where is thy sting	A.T.	A.T.	CT.T.	A.T.
If God be for us	A.	S.	CT.	S.2

In Scheme I the counter-tenor could be replaced by a second woman alto; in Scheme III the counter-tenor could be replaced by a woman alto. (In Scheme III, the version of 'How beautiful' is in the present Appendix; orchestral material may be hired for the arguable transposition of 'Come unto him' to F major in connexion with this scheme. In Scheme IV, Version II of 'Why do the nations' is required.)

These schemes are on the safe side. Though we know that tenor numbers were sometimes taken by a soprano, we do not know how, in that case, the other numbers were distributed. We are also ignorant as to the distribution of other numbers on the occasion(s) when (for example) a tenor took 'Rejoice greatly', or when a boy sang 'Rejoice greatly' and 'I know that my redeemer liveth'.

NOTE (1981) ON THE ORCHESTRAL 'CON/SENZA RIPIENO' MARKS

Notwithstanding my private reservations about their practical validity (they did not, for instance, pass from the Conducting Score into the Foundling Hospital material) these are dutifully reproduced in this edition. But no conductor should feel bound by them, though he may decide to reduce his instrumental forces for certain solo numbers. In my *Textual and Historical Companion* of 1965 I argued (p. 116) for 1749 as the year in which these directions were introduced; subsequently H. D. Clausen, in *Haendels Direktionspartituren* (1972), pp. 58-62, has demonstrated that they refer solely to the conditions of Handel's performance in that one year.

CONTENTS

PART ONE

No. 1. SINFONIA [OVERTURE]*

*An easy arrangement of this movement for pianoforte is published by Novello & Co. Ltd.

29

34

L.H.

39

44

49

54

59   Man.

Ped.

No. 2. RECITATIVE.— COMFORT YE

Isaiah xl, 1-3

Speak ye com-fort-a-bly to Je - ru - sa-lem, speak ye com-fort-a - bly to Je - ru - sa-lem, and cry un-to her, that her war - fare, her war - fare is ac - com-plish'd, that her in - i - qui-ty is par-don'd, i - qui-ty is par-don'd, that her in - i - qui-ty is par - don'd.

Ped. *tutti piano*

B

[tr]

[tr]

wil-der-ness,

The voice of him that crieth in the wil-der-ness, Pre-pare ye the way of the

senza Rip.

forte

30

des-ert

Lord, make straight in the des-ert a high-way for our God.

*

34

[attacca]

No. 3. Air.— EV'RY VALLEY SHALL BE EXALTED

Isaiah xl, 4

Andante
senza Rip.

f

Ped.

piano   forte   piano   forte

5

A

TENOR (or Soprano)

Ev-'ry val-ley,   ev-'ry val-ley—

con Rip.

forte   piano

9

* For recitative cadences, see p.vi.

and the rough pla-ces plain, and the rough pla-ces

67

plain, _____ the

con Rip. [tr]

piano   forte

70

pla - ces E

[tr]

crook-ed straight, and the rough pla - ces plain.

con Rip.

[colla voce]

forte

73

tr tr tr   tr tr tr

piano

77

tr   tr

forte   piano   forte

81

No. 4. Chorus.— AND THE GLORY OF THE LORD

Isaiah xl, 5

14

55

Man.   Ped.

60

C

65

122

128

133

No. 5. Recitative.— THUS SAITH THE LORD

Haggai ii, 6,7; Malachi iii, 1

[attacca]

No. 6. AIR.— BUT WHO MAY ABIDE THE DAY OF HIS COMING?

VERSION I * (The third Version to be composed)

Malachi iii, 2

*Composed in 1750 for the male alto, Gaetano Guadagni. The version originally composed for bass in 1741, which is substantially different and lacks the *prestissimo* sections, is not represented in this edition

22

No. 6.— *VERSION II (Transposition of Version I for Soprano)* *

Larghetto
[senza Rip.]

*This version is to be used exceptionally when the aria is not allotted to an alto (male *or* female) in accordance with Version I.

30

32

No. 7. Chorus.— AND HE SHALL PURIFY

Malachi iii, 3

1) bar 27, alto. Autograph reads

No. 8. Recitative.—BEHOLD, A VIRGIN SHALL CONCEIVE

Isaiah vii, 14; Matthew i, 23

No. 9. Air and Chorus.—O THOU THAT TELLEST GOOD TIDINGS TO ZION

Isaiah xl, 9; lx, 1

un-to the cit-ies of Ju - dah, Be-hold____ your God!____ be-

hold your God! _____ be-hold your God!

forte

O thou that tell-est good ti-dings to Zi-on,

a-rise, shine; for thy light is come,

a - rise,____ a - rise,____ a-rise, shine; for

1) Bar 60. There is a sign here which may be 'p' or 'tr'.

thy light is come, and the glo — — — — — — — ry of the Lord, the glo-ry of the Lord _____ is ris - en,__ is ris - en __ up-on __ thee, is ris - en, is ris - en __ up - on thee, the __ glo-ry, the __ glo-ry, the glo-ry of __ the Lord _____ is ris - en __ up-on thee.

stand.

G

piano

*

AND

*

⌈*⌉ This doubling is perhaps better omitted in performances with piano or organ accompaniment alone.

18725

glo - ry of the Lord ——— is ris - en up - on thee.

Lord ——————————— is ris - en up - on thee.

glo - ry of the Lord ——— is ris - en up - on thee.

glo - ry of the Lord ——— is ris - en up - on thee.

135

139

143

147

No. 10. RECITATIVE.—FOR BEHOLD, DARKNESS SHALL COVER THE EARTH

Isaiah lx, 2, 3

No. 11. AIR.— THE PEOPLE THAT WALKED IN DARKNESS

Isaiah ix, 2

Larghetto

senza Rip.

1) Bar 8. Handel wrote both notes.

18725

No. 12. Chorus.—FOR UNTO US A CHILD IS BORN

Isaiah ix, 6

56

18725

59

18725

62

18725

No. 13 PIFA ["*PASTORAL SYMPHONY*"]

VERSION I – Bars 1-11 only.
VERSION II – Complete. (In this Version
omit bar 11 until the *Da Capo*.)

66

No. 14 (a). Recitative.—THERE WERE SHEPHERDS ABIDING IN THE FIELD
Luke ii, 8

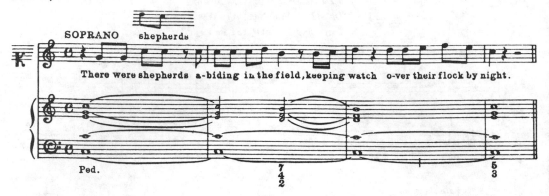

No. 14 (b). Recitative.— AND LO, THE ANGEL OF THE LORD CAME UPON THEM
Luke ii, 9

No. 15. Recitative.— AND THE ANGEL SAID UNTO THEM

Luke ii, 10, 11

No. 16. Recitative.— AND SUDDENLY THERE WAS WITH THE ANGEL

Luke ii, 13

The slurs commonly introduced into the semiquaver figure of the accompaniment to No. 16 are without authority, and are, indeed, ill-suited to the expression of this movement. *Editor*

No. 17. Chorus.— GLORY TO GOD

Luke ii, 14

No. 18. Air.— REJOICE GREATLY, O DAUGHTER OF ZION
VERSION I (*The third Version to be composed*)*

Zechariah ix, 9, 10

Handel's own endorsements on Tenbury MS 346 shew that on one occasion he intended this to be sung by a tenor.

*See Appendix.

* Grace notes from the Autograph (bar 42)

shout, re-joice_____ great-ly,

re-joice _____ greatly, O daughter of Zi - on; shout,___

O daugh-ter of Je - ru-sa-lem: be-hold, thy King com-eth un - to

thee, be-hold, thy King com-eth un - to thee.

[colla voce]

piano forte

78

88

91

95

98

101

104

18725

No. 19. Recitative.— THEN SHALL THE EYES OF THE BLIND

Isaiah xxxv, 5, 6

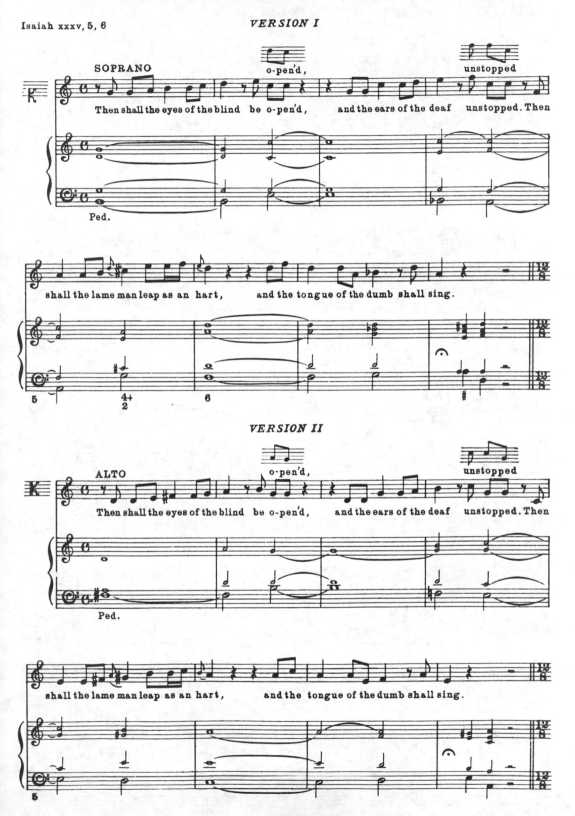

VERSION I

VERSION II

No. 20. AIR.— HE SHALL FEED HIS FLOCK LIKE A SHEPHERD

Isaiah xl, 11; Matthew xi, 28, 29   *VERSION I*

See p.iv on the subject of the keyboard part.

No. 20. – *VERSION II*

Larghetto e piano
[senza Rip.]

ALTO

He shall feed his flock like a shep - herd: and

he __ shall ga - ther the lambs with his arm, with __ his __ arm,

A

he shall feed his flock like a shep - herd: and

he __ shall ga - ther the lambs with his arm, with __ his __ arm,

VERSION II

No. 21. Chorus. — HIS YOKE IS EASY, AND HIS BURTHEN IS LIGHT

Matthew xi, 30

PART TWO

No. 22. Chorus.— BEHOLD THE LAMB OF GOD

John i, 29

92

No. 23. Air.— HE WAS DESPISED *

Isaiah liii, 3; 1,6

*Ornamentation from 'Goldschmidt' MS except in bar 41.

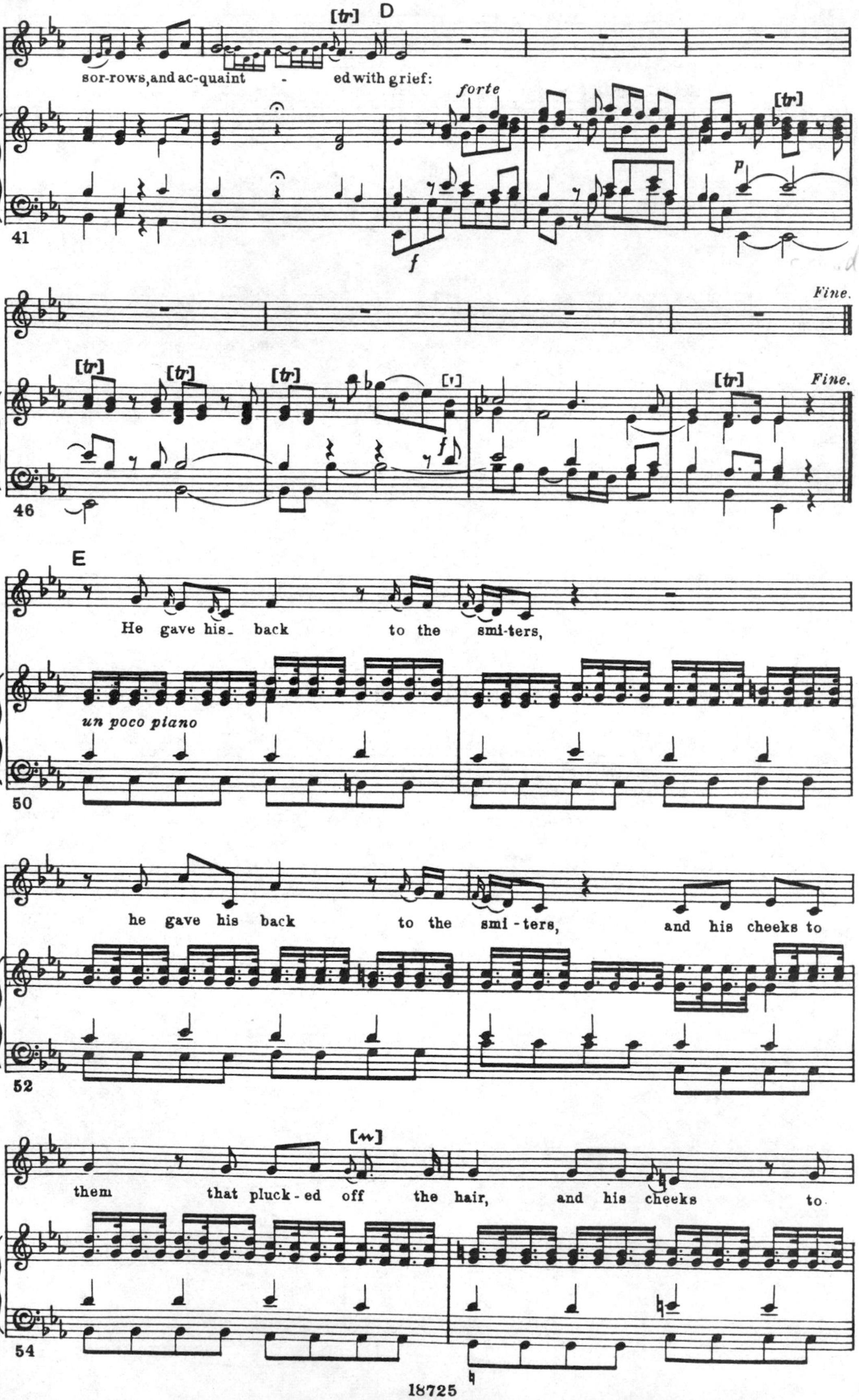

[tr]
D
sor-rows, and ac-quaint - ed with grief:
forte
f
p
[tr]
41
Fine.
Fine.
46
E
He gave his back to the smi-ters,
un poco piano
50
he gave his back to the smi-ters, and his cheeks to
52
them that pluck-ed off the hair, and his cheeks to
54

them that pluck-ed off the hair, and his cheeks to them that plucked off the

F

hair: He hid_ not his face from shame and

spit-ting, he hid not his face from shame, _____

from shame,_____ he hid not his

spit-ting.

D.C.

face from shame, _____ from shame and spit-ting.

D.C.

No. 24. Chorus.— SURELY HE HATH BORNE OUR GRIEFS

Isaiah liii, 4,5

* Handel's key-signature had three flats only; he used accidentals for D flats.

† Handel set this as a word of three syllables:

Sur-e-ly.

100

18725

[attacca]

No. 25. Chorus.— AND WITH HIS STRIPES WE ARE HEALED

Isaiah liii, 5

* Handel's key-signature had three flats only. His time-signature was ¢ with bars of varying length.

18725

*Bar 36. Handel himself wrote both notes.

[attacca]

No. 26. Chorus.— ALL WE LIKE SHEEP HAVE GONE ASTRAY

Isaiah liii, 6

108

18725

64

67

70

*Bar 65. Handel himself wrote both notes.   18725

No. 27. RECITATIVE.—ALL THEY THAT SEE HIM LAUGH HIM TO SCORN

Psalm xxii, 7 (*Book of Common Prayer*)

Psalm xxii, 8 *(Book of Common Prayer)*

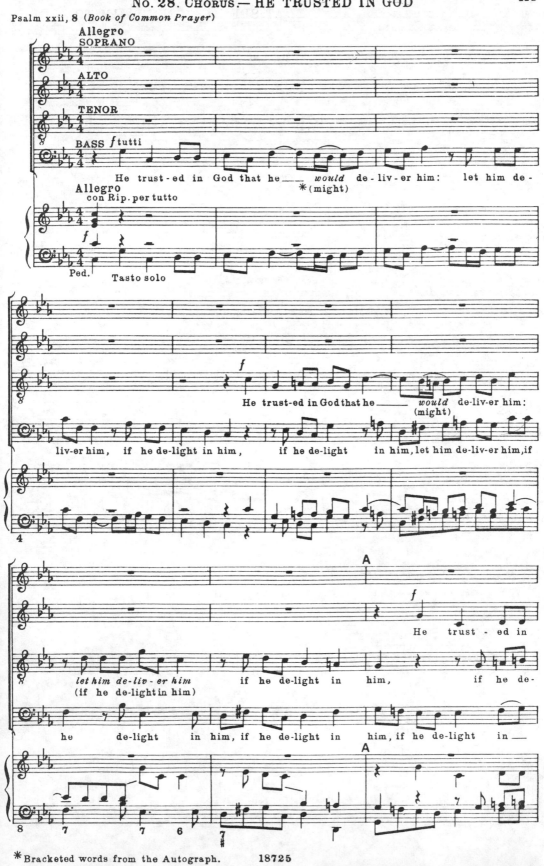

116

18725

18725

sit

No. 29. RECITATIVE.— THY REBUKE HATH BROKEN HIS HEART

Psalm lxix, 21 *(Book of Common Prayer)*

Largo

TENOR (or Soprano)

senza Rip. Thy re - buke hath bro - ken his heart; he is full of heav - i - ness

heav - i - ness, he is full of heav - i - ness: thy re - buke hath bro - ken his heart;

he look - ed for some to have pi - ty on him, but there was no man, neith - er found he a - ny

a - ny to com-fort him, he look - ed for some to have pi - ty on him,

but there was no man, neith - er found he a - ny to com-fort him.

18725

[*attacca*]

No. 30. Air.— BEHOLD, AND SEE IF THERE BE ANY SORROW

Lamentations i, 12

Largo e piano

* Handel's *appoggiatura*

[*attacca*]

No. 31. Recitative.— HE WAS CUT OFF OUT OF THE LAND OF THE LIVING

Isaiah liii, 8

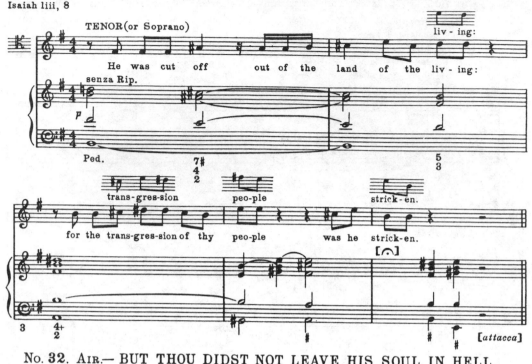

He was cut off out of the land of the liv-ing:

for the trans-gres-sion of thy peo-ple was he strick-en.

[attacca]

No. 32. Air.— BUT THOU DIDST NOT LEAVE HIS SOUL IN HELL

Psalm xvi, 10

Andante larghetto

But thou didst not leave his

soul in hell, but thou didst not leave his

Cut

No. 33. Chorus.— LIFT UP YOUR HEADS, O YE GATES*

Psalm xxiv, 7-10

A tempo ordinario

* In this chorus the division of the alto part is editorial: the style clearly requires the antiphony of *cori spezzati* in the Venetian manner. The division into semi-chorus and chorus, also editorial, is based on the word-books issued in connexion with Handel's Covent Garden performances. (Handel himself adapted this chorus to form an orchestral *Concerto a due cori*.)

128

cut

No. 34. Recitative.—UNTO WHICH OF THE ANGELS SAID HE AT ANY TIME

Hebrews i, 5

No. 35. Chorus.— LET ALL THE ANGELS OF GOD WORSHIP HIM

Hebrews i, 6

*Bar 15. Handel himself wrote both notes.

No. 36. AIR.— THOU ART GONE UP ON HIGH

VERSION I (*The third Version to be composed*)

Psalm lxviii, 18

for__ thine en - - - - - - - - e-mies,yea,

e - ven for thine en - e - mies,

that the Lord God might dwell__ a - mong them, that the Lord

God might dwell _____

_____ a - mong them, might ___ dwell a - mong them.

Thou art gone up on high, thou art gone up on high, thou hast

led cap-ti - vi-ty cap - tive, thou hast led cap-ti - vi - ty cap-tive, and re -

cei - ved, and re - cei - ved gifts for men, and re-

cei - ved gifts for thine en-e-mies, that the Lord God might dwell a -

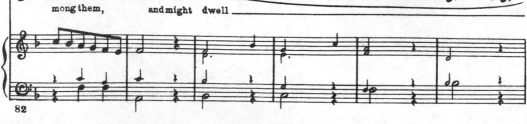

mong them, and might dwell

No. 36.— *VERSION II* (*Transposition of Version I for Soprano*)*

[Allegro Larghetto]
[senza Rip.]

A SOPRANO

Thou art gone up on high, thou art gone up on high,

thou hast led cap-ti - vi-ty cap-tive, thou hast led cap-ti - vi-ty cap-tive, and re-

cei - - - - ved gifts_ for_ men; yea, e - ven

144

a - mong them, that the Lord God,_____ might.

dwell _____ a - mong them,

that the Lord, the Lord God might dwell_____ a - mong them.

No. 37. Chorus.— THE LORD GAVE THE WORD

Psalm lxviii, 11 *(Book of Common Prayer)*

148

No. 38. ARIA.— HOW BEAUTIFUL ARE THE FEET*
VERSION I

Romans x, 15

Larghetto

[senza Rip.]

How beau-ti-ful are the feet of them that preach the gos-pel of peace,_ how beau-ti-ful are the feet, how beau-ti-ful are the feet_ of them that preach the gos-pel of peace, how beau-ti-ful are the feet_ of them that

*See Appendix and *Textual Companion*.   18725

150

preach the gos - pel of peace, and bring glad ti - dings, and

12

bring glad ti - - dings, glad ti - dings of good things, and

14

B

bring glad ti - dings, glad ti - dings of good things, and bring_____ glad ti - dings, glad

16

ti - dings of good things, glad ti - dings of___ good things.

19

22

[attacca]

No. 39. Chorus.—THEIR SOUND IS GONE OUT

Romans x, 18   **VERSION I** (*The third Version to be composed*)

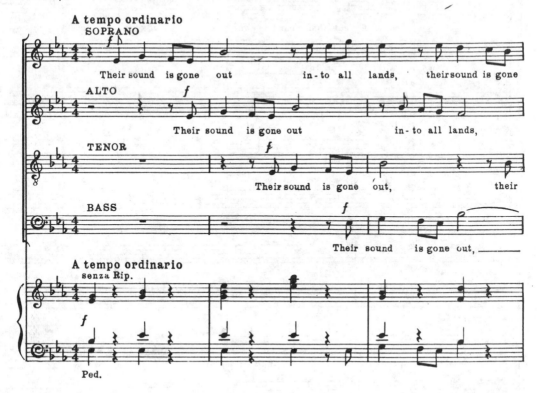

No. 40. Air.— WHY DO THE NATIONS SO FURIOUSLY RAGE TOGETHER?

VERSIONS I & II

Psalm ii, 1, 2 (*Book of Common Prayer*)

-ine_ a_ vain_ thing?_____ im - ag - - - -

B

-ine_ a vain thing?

why do the na - tions so fu - rious-ly rage_ to -

ge - ther: and why do the peo - ple, and

why do the peo - ple im - ag - ine a_ vain_

* Bar 38. For Version II, continue at the Recitative on page 160

18725

158

18725

VERSION II*

* This is not to be thought of as a makeshift ending, but an alternative with authority from Handel's own time. It leads dramatically to the ensuing chorus. *Editor*

162

let us break their bonds a - sunder, let_ us, let_ us break,

sun - der, let us break their

let us break their bonds a - sun-der, let_ us break, let us break their

sun - der, let us break their bonds a -

6

C

let us break their bonds a - sun - der, their bonds a - sun - der, and cast

bonds, let us break their bonds,___ their bonds a - sun - der,

bonds, let us break their bonds a - sun - der, and cast a -

sun - der, let us break their bonds a - sun - der,

C

a - way___ their yokes from

way,___ and cast a - way,___

and cast a - way___

⇨ p170

No. 42. Recitative.— HE THAT DWELLETH IN HEAVEN

Psalm ii, 4 (*Book of Common Prayer*)

dwelleth in hea-ven

de-ri-sion

He that dwelleth in hea-ven shall laugh them to scorn: the Lord shall have them in de-ri-sion.

Psalm ii, 9

No. 43. Air.— THOU SHALT BREAK THEM

Andante
senza Rip.

TENOR A

Thou shalt break them, thou shalt

break them with a rod of i - ron;

pot - ter's ves - sel, thou shalt dash them in

pie - ces like a pot - - ter's

D

ves - sel.

forte

Rev. xix, 6 – xi, 15; xix, 16

*Handel himself wrote both notes

er, KING OF KINGS, AND LORD OF LORDS, Hal-le-lu-jah, Hal-le-

er, for ev-er and ev-er, for ev-er and ev-er, Hal-le-lu-jah, Hal-le-

er, for ev-er and ev-er, for ev-er and ev-er, Hal-le-lu-jah, Hal-le-

er, for ev-er and ev-er, for ev-er and ev-er, Hal-le-lu-jah, Hal-le-

Trumpets

Str.

88

lu-jah, Hal-le-lu-jah, Hal-le-lu-jah, Hal - le - lu - jah!

lu-jah, Hal-le-lu-jah, Hal-le-lu-jah, Hal - le - lu - jah!

lu-jah, Hal-le-lu-jah, Hal-le-lu-jah, Hal - le - lu - jah!

lu-jah, Hal-le-lu-jah, Hal-le-lu-jah, Hal - le - lu - jah!

Tutti

91

PART THREE

No. 45. AIR.– I KNOW THAT MY REDEEMER LIVETH *

Job xix, 25, 26; 1 Cor. xv, 20

* Ornamentation from 'Goldschmidt' MS. 18725

1) Bar 126. This is Handel's original form, which he afterwards changed to:

first - fruits of them that sleep,

18725

2) Bar 134. This is Handel's original form, which he afterwards changed to:

first - fruits of them that sleep. *etc.*

3) Bar 149. Handel's text is as follows, with nothing to shew how 'them' and 'that' are to be treated:

the first-fruits of— them that sleep. *etc.*

J. C. Smith, in the first fair copy (Tenbury MS), hazarded:

the first - fruits of them that sleep. *etc.*

The present Editor ventures a reading of his own, close to that in Add. MS 5062.

No. 46. Chorus.— SINCE BY MAN CAME DEATH

I Cor. xv, 21, 22

No. 47. RECITATIVE.— BEHOLD, I TELL YOU A MYSTERY

I Cor. xv, 51-52

No. 48. AIR.— THE TRUMPET SHALL SOUND

I Cor. xv, 52-54

1) Bar 38. Handel wrote: ♯ *etc.*

rais'd in - cor - rup - ti - ble

2) Bar 51. Handel wrote: in-cor-rup-ti-ble *etc.*
(see also Bars 91-93.)

3) Bar 54. Handel wrote: in-cor-rup-ti-ble *etc.*
'see also Bars 94-96.)

194

Adagio   G [a tempo]

we shall   be changed.

[colla voce]   forte   Strings   Trumpet

189

[tr]   Trumpet   Strings   Trumpet

145

FINE

For this cor-

Man. II. 8'

Strings   tr

151   Man. I. 16'+8'

rup - ti - ble must put— on in - cor - rup-tion,   for

158

this   cor - rup - ti - ble must   put   on,   must put on,———

165

must put on, must put on in - cor - rup-tion,

172

and this mor - tal must put____ on im-mor-

179

tal - - - - - - -

186

- - - i - ty, and this mor-tal must put on im-mor-

198

tal - - - - - - - - - -

200

No. 49. RECITATIVE.– THEN SHALL BE BROUGHT TO PASS

I Cor. xv, 54

Nos. 50-51. DUET.– O DEATH, WHERE IS THY STING?
CHORUS.– BUT THANKS BE TO GOD

I Cor. xv, 55-57

198

Segue chorus

No. 51. *CHORUS*

No. 52. Air.— IF GOD BE FOR US

VERSION I

Romans viii, 31, 33-34

1) Bars 26/7 Handel wrote   God be for us   2) Bars 38/9 Handel wrote   God is for us

for us, who can be a-gainst us?

B

Who shall lay_ a-ny-thing to the charge of

God's e-lect?_____ of God's e-lect?

who shall lay a-ny-thing to the charge_____

of_ God's e-lect?

210

right hand of God, who is at the right hand of God, at the right hand of

Adagio   3)   [tr]   [a tempo]

God,   who makes in-ter-ces - sion for us.

forte

152

158

164

169

174

3) Bar 161. Handel wrote

-ces-sion for

No. 52. — *VERSION II* *(Transposition of Version I for Alto)*

214

who is he that con-demn-eth, who is he that con-demn - - - - - eth? It is Christ that di-ed, yea ra-ther, that is ri-sen a-gain, who is at the right hand of God, who

18725

right hand of God, who is at the right hand of God, at the right hand of

Adagio *tr* **[a tempo]**

God, who makes in - ter - ces - sion for _ us.

Revelation v, 12, 13

* Bar 39. It has recently been shown by Donald Burrows that this 'cut' relates not to 'Messiah' but to Handel's adaptation of this movement for his 'Anthem on the Peace'. (1981).

222

18725

228

men, A

A men, A

A men, A men,

men,

119

men, A men, A

men, A men, A

A men,

A men, A

123   5   6   4   8   7   6

men, A

men, A men, A men. A

A men, A men,

men, A men, A men, A

127   7   6   4   #   7   7   4   #
                                5
                                3

18725

144

148

153

APPENDIX
[No. 18.] Air.– REJOICE GREATLY, O DAUGHTER OF ZION
VERSION II (The second Version to be composed)

*Handel's own common-time notation of this 12-8 bass has been preserved here. Crotchets and crotchet rests should be read as dotted; other conventions are interpreted by the Editor by means of the rhythmic signs.

be - hold, thy King cometh un - to thee,___ com-eth [sic]

un - to thee. *forte*

piano *forte* He is___ the___ *piano*

piano

righ - teous Sa - - vi-our,

* Here Handel cut out 48 bars of the original form of this movement, and slightly changed the following bar to the form now given.

*In its original form this bar simply contained the harmony of D minor for voice and *continuo* only, followed by the direction '*Da Capo*'. Handel altered it as now given to provide a link to a modified re-statement (bars 66 to first half of 69) of the opening (*cf.* bars 1-3 and 9-11), and then proceeded to use the last 39 bars of the section cut out as marked at bar 44 above.

[No. 36.] Air.— THOU ART GONE UP ON HIGH
VERSION III (*The first Version to be composed*)

might dwell a-mong them.

C

forte

Thou art gone up on high, thou art gone up on high, thou hast

legato

led cap-tiv-i-ty cap-tive, thou hast led cap-tiv-i-ty cap-tive,

and re-ceiv-ed gifts for men: yea, e-ven

piano

for thine en - - - -

tr

242

18725

[No. 38.] Air.—HOW BEAUTIFUL ARE THE FEET
VERSION II

* These *appoggiature* are from the source. Handel's autograph copy of this version does not survive. See *Textual Companion*.

18725

ti - dings of _good things, and bring glad ti dings, glad

ti - dings of good things, and bring ___ glad ti - dings, glad ___

ti - dings, glad ti - dings of __ good things.

[cf No. 38.] Duet and Chorus.– HOW BEAUTIFUL ARE THE FEET

Isaiah lii, 7,9

* When desired, this part may be sung by a soprano, observing the octave transpositions noted. In such case the octave transposition noted in bars 40-43 of Alto 1 must be observed. This has Handel's authority.

him! that bring - eth *glad (good)* ti - dings, that bring - eth

How beau - ti - ful are the feet of him that bring - eth

how beau - ti - ful are the feet that

bring-eth good ti-dings, that bring - eth

110

ti - - dings of sal - va - - - - tion;

ti - - dings of sal - va - tion, of sal - va - tion;

bring ti - dings of sal - va - tion, of sal - va - tion;

ti - - dings of sal - va - - - tion;

116

that saith un - to

that saith un - to

that saith un - to

that saith un - to

[No. 39] AIR.— THEIR SOUND IS GONE OUT
VERSION II (*The second Version to be composed*)

Romans x, 18